Back to Basics

MATHS

for 7-8 year olds

BOOK ONE

George Rodda

Letts

Addition tables

 Check the additions in this table.

+	2	4
1	3	5
2	4	6

$1 + 2 = 3$

$1 + 4 = 5$

$2 + 2 = 4$

$2 + 4 = 6$

Fill in these addition tables.

+	3	6	9	12	15
3					
6			15		
9					
12				24	

+	3	5	7
3			
5			
7			
9			

+	7	9	11
7			
9			
11			
13			

+	8	11	14
8			
11			
14			

+	10	13	16
10			
13			
16			

+	11	14	17
11			
14			
17			

+	0	4	8	12	16
0					
4					
8					
12					

+	0	1	2	3	4	5
10						
11						
12						
13						

Length

Ian's handspan is

quite small.

It is 10 cm long.

 Fill in the missing numbers for Ian's handspan.

Number of spans	1	2		6	5	3	7
Length	10 cm	cm	40 cm	cm	50 cm	cm	cm

Use Ian's span of 10 cm.

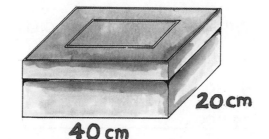

This box is _____ spans long

and _____ spans wide.

 Write in the lengths in cm.

A frog is ½ span long. _____ cm

A newt is 1½ spans long. _____ cm

A snake is 2½ spans long. _____ cm

A frog and a snake together

would be _____ spans long.

A snake and a newt together

would be _____ spans long.

A snake is _____ spans or _____ cm longer than a frog.

Words for numbers

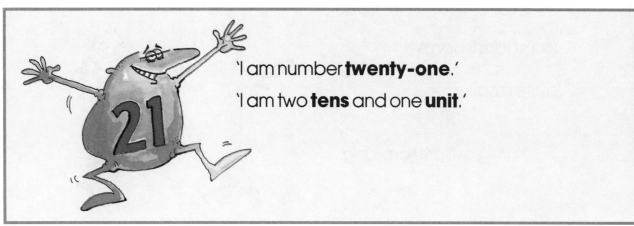

'I am number **twenty-one**.'

'I am two **tens** and one **unit**.'

Write these in figures.

1 thirty-two   **2** sixty-six   **3** thirteen   **4** forty-four

_____   _____   _____   _____

5 one hundred and one _____   **6** ninety-nine _____

Write these numbers in words.

7 41 _____   **8** 33 _____

9 19 _____   **10** 43 _____

11 99 _____   **12** 70 _____

Write in words the value
of the number in blue.

13 120 _____   **14** 374 _____

15 446 _____   **16** 627 _____

17 102 _____   **18** 962 _____

Write in words the value
of the number in red.

19 789 _____   **20** 789 _____

21 789 _____   **22** 879 _____

Taking away

A bus has 19 people on it   19

          7 people get off   −7

     12 are left on the bus   12

 Finish these sums.

$9 - 5 =$ ☐	$12 - 5 =$ ☐	$15 - 5 =$ ☐
$10 - 5 =$ ☐	$13 - 5 =$ ☐	$16 - 5 =$ ☐
$11 - 5 =$ ☐	$14 - 5 =$ ☐	$17 - 5 =$ ☐
$10 - 8 =$ ☐	$13 - 8 =$ ☐	$16 - 8 =$ ☐
$11 - 8 =$ ☐	$14 - 8 =$ ☐	$17 - 8 =$ ☐
$12 - 8 =$ ☐	$15 - 8 =$ ☐	$18 - 8 =$ ☐

$$\begin{array}{cccccc} 19 & 28 & 23 & 13 & 28 & 33 \\ -7 & -20 & -19 & -4 & -18 & -12 \\ \hline \end{array}$$

$$\begin{array}{cccccc} 20 & 17 & 28 & 22 & 20 & 28 \\ -11 & -9 & -19 & -12 & -4 & -17 \\ \hline \end{array}$$

Shapes

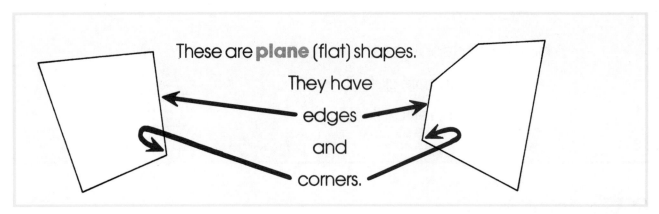

These are **plane** (flat) shapes.
They have
edges
and
corners.

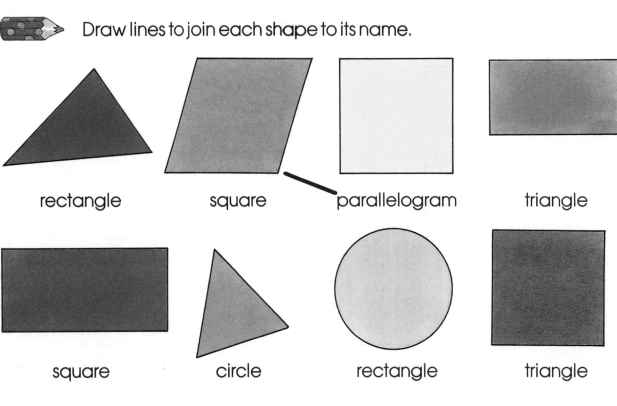

Draw lines to join each shape to its name.

rectangle   square   parallelogram   triangle

square   circle   rectangle   triangle

Write in the numbers and name for each shape.

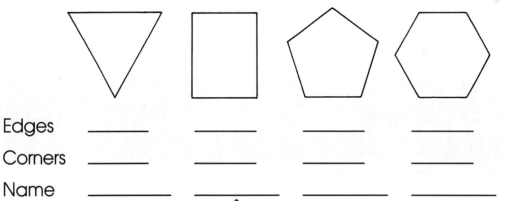

Edges   _____   _____   _____   _____

Corners   _____   _____   _____   _____

Name   _____   _____   _____   _____

Addition patterns

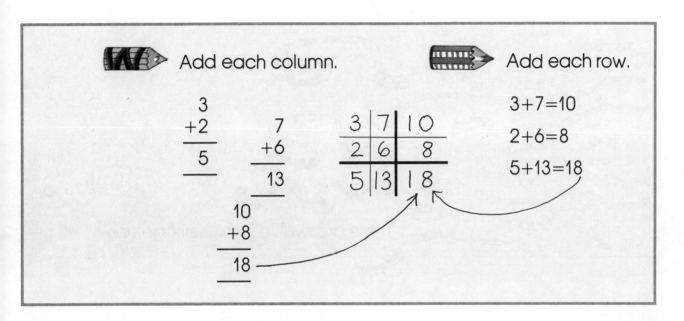

Add each column.

$$\begin{array}{r} 3 \\ +2 \\ \hline 5 \end{array}$$

$$\begin{array}{r} 7 \\ +6 \\ \hline 13 \end{array}$$

$$\begin{array}{r} 10 \\ +8 \\ \hline 18 \end{array}$$

3	7	10
2	6	8
5	13	18

Add each row.

3+7=10

2+6=8

5+13=18

 Fill in these addition squares.

6	5	
5	4	
		20

8	10	
2	2	

9	11	
4	3	

3	1	1	
3	5	1	
4	2	2	

5	2	3	
1	7	2	
2	2	3	

6	5	1	
4	4	4	
3	1	1	

3	2	1	5	
4	1	5	2	
2	5	4	1	
1	2	4	4	

1	2	3	4	
1	2	3	4	
1	2	3	4	
1	2	3	4	

3	3	3	3	
5	5	5	5	
4	4	4	4	
2	2	2	2	

Addition

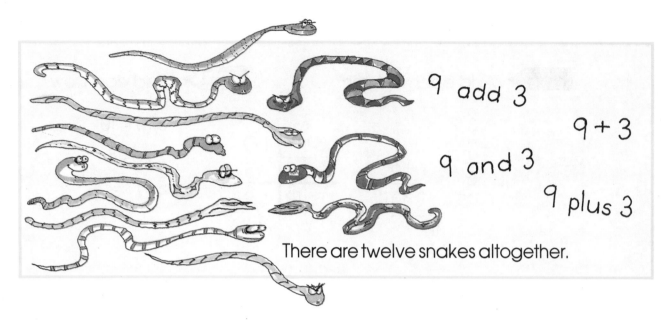

9 add 3

9 + 3

9 and 3

9 plus 3

There are twelve snakes altogether.

 Find the total.

1 27
     +32
    ___

    ___

2 47
     +23
    ___

    ___

3 26
     +34
    ___

    ___

4 126
     +280
    ___

    ___

5 23+17

  = ___

6 38 add 51

  = ___

7 62 and 29

  make ___

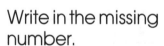 Write in the missing number.

8 The total score for the three red darts is ___

9 The total score for the three blue darts is ___

10 The total score for the six darts is ___

11 Draw 3 black darts to score 80.

12 Draw 3 green darts to score 120.

Ten pence

This 10p coin can be exchanged for one 2p coin and eight 1p coins.

10p → [1] 2p and [8] 1p

Write the number in each box.

10p → [ ] 2p and [6] 1p   10p → [ ] 2p and [4] 1p

10p → [ ] 2p and [2] 1p   10p → [4] 2p and [ ] 1p

10p → [ ] 5p and [5] 1p   10p → [ ] 5p

10p → [ ] 2p and [1] 1p and [ ] 5p

Write the coin value in each circle.

10p → [10] p   10p → [2] p

10p → [3] p and [4] p   10p → [1] p and [5] p

10p → [1] p and [1] p and [3] p

Subtraction

Someone has taken 4 cakes.

9 – 4

subtract 4 from 9

9 minus 4

9 take away 4

There are 5 cakes left.

 Work these out.

1   28
     –17
     ——

2   46
     –17
     ——

3   34
     –17
     ——

4 123
     –24
     ——

5 32–9

= ——

6 41 take away 20

= ——

7 39 minus 19

= ——

8 Subtract 15 from 40

——

9 427 take away 419

——

Tom's newspaper round is:

High Road	15 papers
Low Road	38 papers
Main Street	57 papers

 Write in the missing numbers.

10 Tom delivers ___ more papers in Main Street than Low Road.

11 Tom delivers ___ less papers in High Road than Low Road.

12 Tom delivers ___ less papers in High Road than Main Street.

A number line

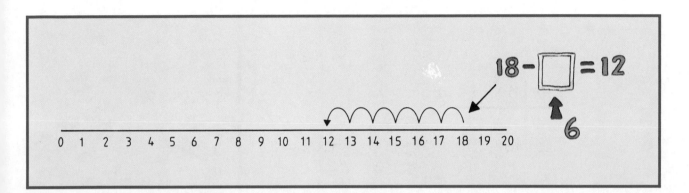

$$18 - \boxed{} = 12$$

 Use the number line to help you fill in the missing numbers.

1 $16 + 2 = \boxed{}$ **2** $9 + 9 = \boxed{}$ **3** $9 + 8 = \boxed{}$

4 $16 - 2 = \boxed{}$ **5** $9 - 9 = \boxed{}$ **6** $9 - 8 = \boxed{}$

7 $7 + \boxed{} = 15$ **8** $15 - \boxed{} = 7$ **9** $15 - \boxed{} = 8$

10 $13 + \boxed{} = 17$ **11** $17 - \boxed{} = 13$ **12** $17 - 13 = \boxed{}$

13 $18 - 11 = \boxed{}$ **14** $11 + 7 = \boxed{}$ **15** $18 - 7 = \boxed{}$

16 $14 - \boxed{} = 11$ **17** $14 + \boxed{} = 19$ **18** $14 - \boxed{} = 9$

19
```
  10
-  3
────
```

20
```
   18
-  ▢
────
   17
```

21
```
   19
-  ▢
────
   18
```

22
```
   18
+  ▢
────
   20
```

23
```
   11
+  ▢
────
   20
```

24
```
   12
+  ▢
────
   20
```

25
```
   13
+  ▢
────
   20
```

26
```
   14
+  ▢
────
   20
```

27 I have 20p and spend 9p. I have $\boxed{}$ p left.

28 I started shopping with 20p and now have 16p left.

I spent $\boxed{}$ p.

Multiplication tables

$$4 \times 2 = 8$$

$$4 \times 3 = 12$$

X	2	3
4	8	12
5	10	15

$$5 \times 2 = 10$$

$$5 \times 3 = 15$$

 Fill in these multiplication tables.

X	2	3	4
2	4		
3			
4			
5			20

X	7	8	9
3			
4			
5			
6			

X	0	2	4	6
0				
2				
4				
6				

X	1	3	5	7
1				
3				
5				
7				

X	6	8	10	12
1				
2				
3				
4				
5				

X	5	7	9
1			
2			
3			
4			
5			

X	1	2	3	4
5				
9				
6				

X	3	2	6	5
3				
5				
7				

X	3	4	5	6
2				
4				
6				

Fractions

Here are four spiders.

1 of them is green. So ¼ is green.

3 of them are red. So ¾ are red.

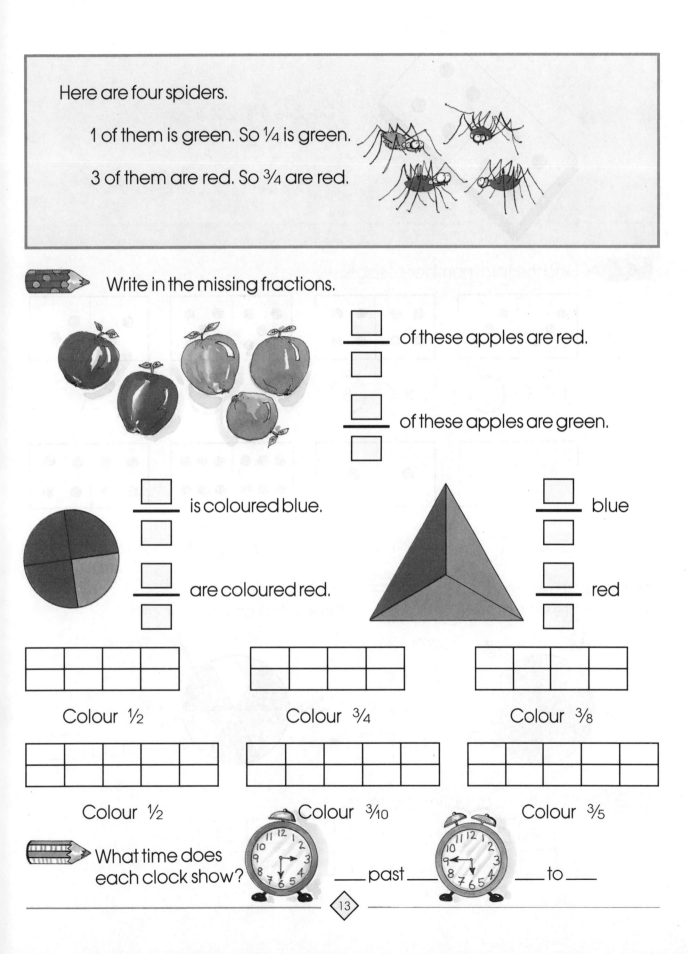

Write in the missing fractions.

⬜/⬜ of these apples are red.

⬜/⬜ of these apples are green.

⬜/⬜ is coloured blue.

⬜/⬜ are coloured red.

⬜/⬜ blue

⬜/⬜ red

Colour ½

Colour ¾

Colour ⅜

Colour ½

Colour ³⁄₁₀

Colour ⅗

What time does each clock show? ___ past ___ ___ to ___

13

Doubling

Double 4 is 2×4

$= 8$

 Find the total number of spots.

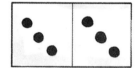

$2 \times 3 = \bigcirc$

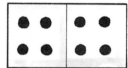

$2 \times 4 = \boxed{8}$

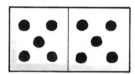

$2 \times 5 = \bigcirc$

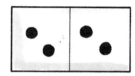

$2 \times 2 = \bigcirc$

$2 \times 0 = \bigcirc$

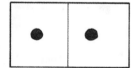

$2 \times 1 = \bigcirc$

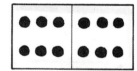

$2 \times 6 = \bigcirc$

$2 \times 4 = \bigcirc$

The red parts on these boards score **double.**

 Find the total for the three darts on each board.

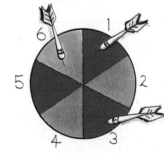

Score: 2×1

$+ 6$

$+ 2 \times 3$

Total $\boxed{}$

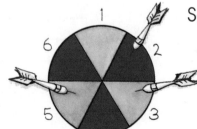

Score:

$+$

$+$

Total $\boxed{}$

 Fill in these doubling patterns.

$1, 2, 4, \boxed{}, 16$ $3, \boxed{}, \boxed{}, 24$

$5, \boxed{}, 20, \boxed{}$ $7, \boxed{}, 28, \boxed{}$

Using twelve

Pat says that it is time
for lunch.

It is five past twelve.

 Fill in the missing numbers.

$10 + \boxed{} = 12$ $\qquad$ $2 + \boxed{} = 12$ $\qquad$ $12 - 10 = \boxed{}$

$12 - 2 = \boxed{}$ $\qquad$ $12 + \boxed{} = 22$ $\qquad$ $12 - 8 = \boxed{}$

 Finish drawing 12
counters to make a
6 by **2** pattern.

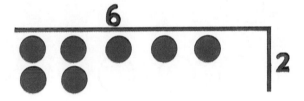

 Draw counters for a
2 by **6** pattern.

Draw counters for a
3 by **4** pattern.

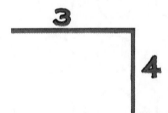

Draw counters for a
4 by **3** pattern.

Multilication

$$6 \times 2 = 2 + 2 + 2 + 2 + 2 + 2 = 12$$
$$4 \times 6 = 6 + 6 + 6 + 6 = 24$$

 Fill in the missing numbers and work out the answers.

1 $4 \times 3 = 3 +$ ⃝ $+$ ⃝ $+$ ⃝

= ☐

2 $4 \times 5 = 5 +$ ⃝ $+$ ⃝ $+$ ⃝

= ☐

3 $4 \times 2 =$ ⃝ $+$ ⃝ $+$ ⃝ $+$ ⃝

= ☐

4 $2 \times 6 =$ ⃝ $+$ ⃝

= ☐

5 $3 \times 10 =$ ⃝ $+$ ⃝ $+$ ⃝

= ☐

6 $3 \times 8 =$ ⃝ $+$ ⃝ $+$ ⃝

= ☐

7 $6 \times 5 =$ ⃝ $+$ ⃝ $+$ ⃝ $+$ ⃝ $+$ ⃝ $+$ ⃝ $=$ ☐

8 $5 \times 6 =$ ⃝ $+$ ⃝ $+$ ⃝ $+$ ⃝ $+$ ⃝ $=$ ☐

9 $7 \times 4 =$ ⃝ $+$ ⃝ $+$ ⃝ $+$ ⃝ $+$ ⃝ $+$ ⃝ $+$ ⃝ $=$ ☐

10 $5 \times 3 =$ ☐

11 $3 \times 5 =$ ☐

12 $4 \times 4 =$ ☐

13 $2 \times 9 =$ ☐

14 $9 \times 2 =$ ☐

15 $2 \times 10 =$ ☐

16 $6 \times 3 =$ ☐

17 $4 \times 6 =$ ☐

18 $3 \times 7 =$ ☐

Fractions

Ian's share of the cake is one quarter.

Ian's share:

$\frac{1}{4}$

 Use the lines on this cake to help you shade ½ of it red and ⅓ of it blue.

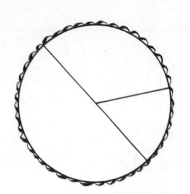

 Use a ruler to measure the length of each piece of string.

 Mark **X** on each piece of string to show:

Length

_____ cm ———————————————————— ½ of it

_____ cm —————————————— ½ of it

_____ cm ———————————————— ⅓ of it

_____ cm ——————————— ¼ of it

This box contains 12 pieces of fudge.

 Fill in the answers.

½ of the box contains ____ pieces

¼ of the box contains ____ pieces

¾ of the box contains ____ pieces

⅓ of the box contains ____ pieces

Time

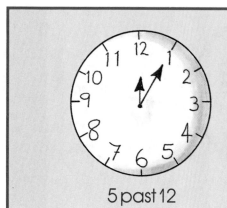 

5 past 12   10 past 12

The difference in time between these clocks is 5 minutes.

 Use the clock faces to help you write down the number of minutes between the two times.

2 o'clock
and 10 past 2.

_____ minutes

2 o'clock
and a quarter past 2.

_____ minutes

2 o'clock
and 20 past 2.

_____ minutes

A quarter past 1
and half past 1.

_____ minutes

Half past 1
and a quarter to 2.

_____ minutes

1 o'clock
and 2 o'clock.

_____ minutes

 Draw an arrow round each clock face to show

clockwise    anti-clockwise

My watch is 10 minutes **fast**. It shows 12 o'clock.

The time is _____

My watch is 15 minutes **slow**. It shows ½ past 1.

The time is _____

More or less

4 is **more than** 2

3 is **less than** 7

6 is **equal to** 2 × 3

 Put in the correct words from

is more than   **is less than**   **is equal to**

3 × 3 ⬚ 2 × 3   2 × 2 ⬚ 2 × 2

5 × 3 ⬚ 6 × 2   3 + 3 ⬚ 3 × 3

10 × 0 ⬚ 0 × 6   4 × 5 ⬚ 2 × 10

 Write down the total length.

4 spans of 20 cm   4 spans of 21 cm   4 spans of 19 cm

= _____ cm   = _____ cm   = _____ cm

Which answer is more than the other two? _____ cm

Which answer is less than the other two? _____ cm

What is my number?

My number is 3 less than 5 × 3. It is _____

My number is 5 more than 3 × 5. It is _____

My number is 7 more than 6 + 7. It is _____

My number is less than 4 × 2 but more than 2 × 3.

It is _____

Millimetres (mm) and centimetres (cm)

___ This line is 1 cm or 10 mm long.

_____ This line is 2 cm or 20 mm long.

_____ This line is 3 cm or 30 mm long.

Write these lengths in mm.

1 4 cm
= ☐ mm

2 5 cm
= ☐ mm

3 6 cm
= ☐ mm

4 7 cm
= ☐ mm

5 8 cm
= ☐ mm

6 9 cm
= ☐ mm

7 ½ cm
= ☐ mm

8 2½ cm
= ☐ mm

9 $\frac{1}{10}$ cm
= ☐ mm

Write these mm as cm.

1 30 mm
= ☐ cm

2 10 mm
= ☐ cm

3 15 mm
= ☐ cm

Add these mm and change the answers to cm.

1 5 mm
+ 15 mm
___ mm = ☐ cm

2 25 mm
+ 15 mm
___ mm = ☐ cm

3 14 mm
+ 16 mm
___ mm = ☐ cm

4 20 mm
23 mm
+ 37 mm
___ mm = ☐ cm

Days and dates

July					
Mon		7	14	21	28
Tues	1	8	15	22	29
Wed	2	9	16	23	30
Thurs	3	10	17	24	31
Fri	4	11	18	25	
Sat	5	12	19	26	
Sun	6	13	20	27	

This is a calendar page for July

 Answer these questions.

How many days are there in July? _____ days

What is the day

7 days after Thursday 3rd July? _____ day

The date will then be _____ July.

What is the day

5 days after Thursday 3rd July? _____ day

The date will then be _____ July.

What is the day

6 days before Friday 18th July? _____ day

The date will then be _____ July.

On this calendar page shade in red all the **odd** numbers.

November					
Mon		5	12	19	26
Tues		6	13	20	27
Wed		7	14	21	28
Thurs	1	8	15	22	29
Fri	2	9	16	23	30
Sat	3	10	17	24	
Sun	4	11	18	25	

On this calendar page shade in blue all the **even** numbers.

February					
Mon		5	12	19	26
Tues		6	13	20	27
Wed		7	14	21	28
Thurs	1	8	15	22	
Fri	2	9	16	23	
Sat	3	10	17	24	
Sun	4	11	18	25	

Sharing

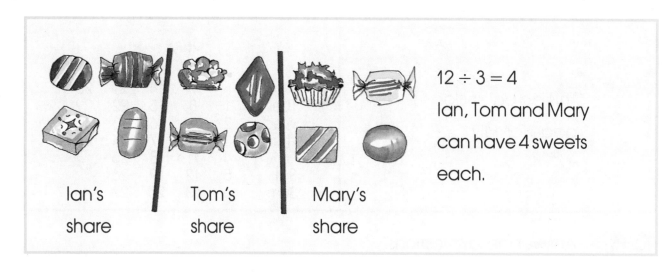

$12 \div 3 = 4$

Ian, Tom and Mary can have 4 sweets each.

Ian's share | Tom's share | Mary's share

 Write down the answers.

1 $8 \div 4$
= ☐

2 $8 \div 2$
= ☐

3 $12 \div 2$
= ☐

4 $12 \div 6$
= ☐

5 $15 \div 3$
= ☐

6 $15 \div 5$
= ☐

7 $16 \div 2$
= ☐

8 $16 \div 4$
= ☐

9 $14 \div 2$
= ☐

10 $14 \div 7$
= ☐

11 $18 \div 9$
= ☐

12 $18 \div 2$
= ☐

13 $35 \div 5$
= ____

14 $21 \div 3$
= ____

15 $28 \div 4$
= ____

16 $28 \div 7$
= ____

17 Ian and Mary share 18 apples.

How many do they have each? ____ apples

18 Tom, Mary and Ian have equal shares of 27 apples.

How many do they have each? ____ apples

 Fill in the missing numbers.

19 $8 \div \boxed{} = 2$

20 $10 \div \boxed{} = 5$

Weight

You can weigh yourself
on scales like these.

Mr Jones weighs 120kg,

Mrs Jones weighs 65kg,

Tammy weighs 35kg

and Ian weighs 40kg.

 Find the total weight for:

1 Mrs Jones 65 kg
   Tammy + 35 kg
   _____ kg

2 Tammy ____ kg
   Ian + ____ kg
   _____ kg

3 Mr Jones ____ kg
   Mrs Jones + ____ kg
   _____ kg

4 Mr Jones ____ kg
   Ian + ____ kg
   _____ kg

5 Mr Jones ____ kg
   Tammy + ____ kg
   _____ kg

6 Mrs Jones ____ kg
   Ian + ____ kg
   _____ kg

 Find the difference in weight for:

7 Mrs Jones ____ kg
   Tammy − ____ kg
   _____ kg

8 Ian ____ kg
   Tammy − ____ kg
   _____ kg

9 Mr Jones ____ kg
   Mrs Jones − ____ kg
   _____ kg

10 Mrs Jones ____ kg
   Ian − ____ kg
   _____ kg

11 Mr Jones ____ kg
   Ian − ____ kg
   _____ kg

12 Mr Jones ____ kg
   Tammy − ____ kg
   _____ kg

13 Find the total weight
of the family.   120 kg + 65 kg + 35 kg + 40 kg = _____ kg

Twenty pence

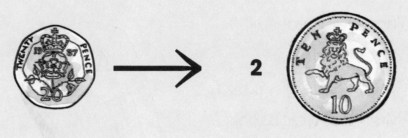

20p can be made up from two 10p coins.

 Write the number of coins needed in each box.

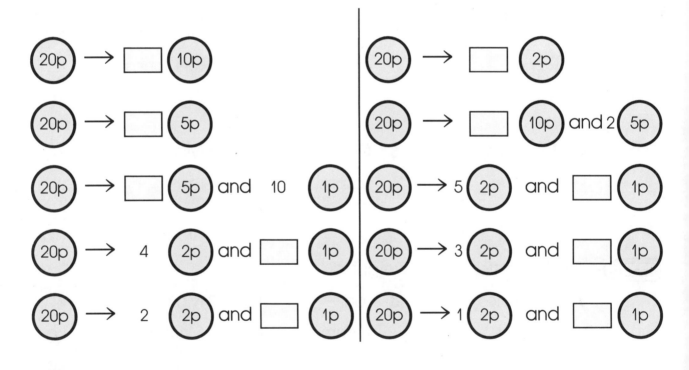

(20p) → [ ] (10p)   (20p) → [ ] (2p)

(20p) → [ ] (5p)   (20p) → [ ] (10p) and 2 (5p)

(20p) → [ ] (5p) and 10 (1p)   (20p) → 5 (2p) and [ ] (1p)

(20p) → 4 (2p) and [ ] (1p)   (20p) → 3 (2p) and [ ] (1p)

(20p) → 2 (2p) and [ ] (1p)   (20p) → 1 (2p) and [ ] (1p)

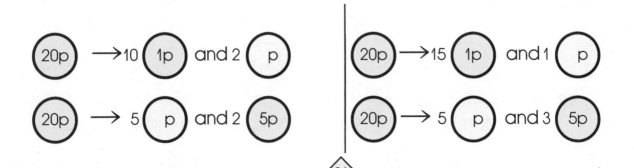 Write the coin value in each circle.

(20p) → 10 (1p) and 2 (p)   (20p) → 15 (1p) and 1 (p)

(20p) → 5 (p) and 2 (5p)   (20p) → 5 (p) and 3 (5p)

Squares

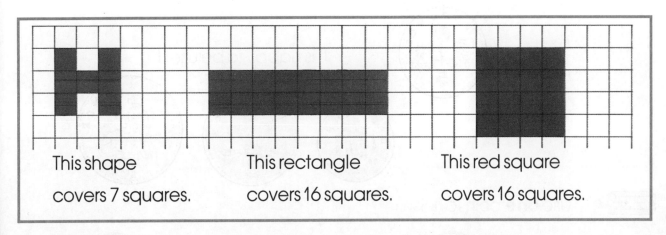

This shape covers 7 squares.

This rectangle covers 16 squares.

This red square covers 16 squares.

✏️ How many squares are covered by these shapes?

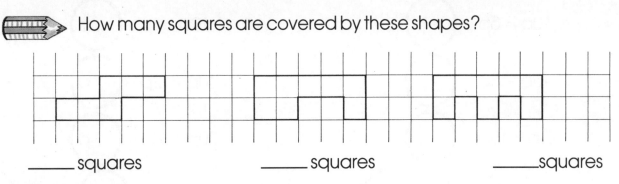

_____ squares   _____ squares   _____ squares

✏️ On these squares draw a letter:

covering **5** squares   covering **6** squares   covering **7** squares

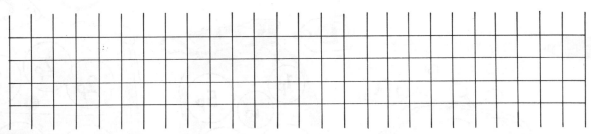
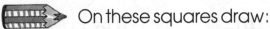

✏️ On these squares draw:

a **rectangle** covering **8** small squares

a **rectangle** covering **14** small squares

a **square** covering **9** small squares

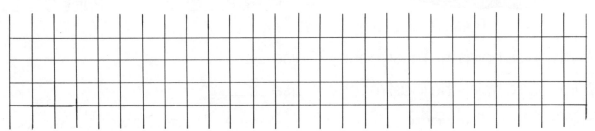

Money

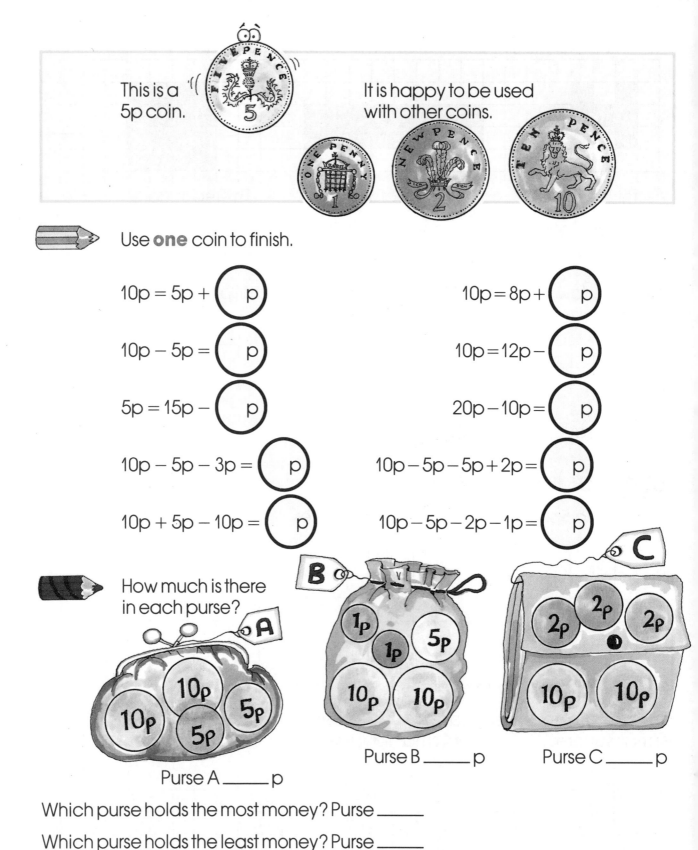

This is a 5p coin.

It is happy to be used with other coins.

Use **one** coin to finish.

10p = 5p + (p)

10p − 5p = (p)

5p = 15p − (p)

10p − 5p − 3p = (p)

10p + 5p − 10p = (p)

10p = 8p + (p)

10p = 12p − (p)

20p − 10p = (p)

10p − 5p − 5p + 2p = (p)

10p − 5p − 2p − 1p = (p)

How much is there in each purse?

Purse A _____ p

Purse B _____ p

Purse C _____ p

Which purse holds the most money? Purse _____

Which purse holds the least money? Purse _____

Purse B − Purse C is worth _____ p   Purse A − Purse C is worth _____ p

Graphs

This is a graph showing how Ian spends his day.

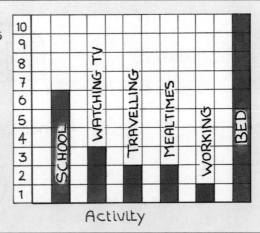

 Write down the number of hours for Ian.

Bed _____ hours   School _____ hours

Watching TV _____ hours   Travelling _____ hours

Mealtimes _____ hours   Working _____ hours

The total time spent by Ian at school and in bed is _____ hours.

The total time spent by Ian travelling and eating is _____ hours.

 Finish drawing this block graph showing the number of people in each of these families.

Number in family:

Smith	8
Jones	3
Brown	7
Aziz	5
M'Ginty	4
Petra	5

Family Size

Family names: Smith, Jones, Brown, Aziz, M'Ginty, Petra

Solids

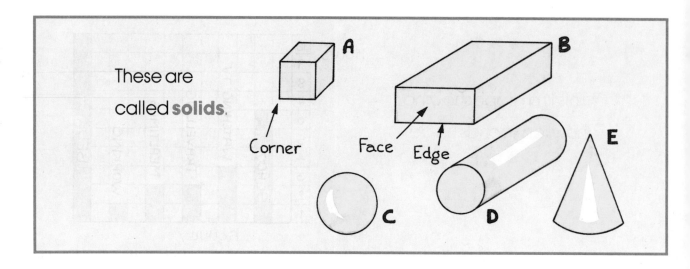

These are called **solids**.

Corner   Face   Edge

The names of the solids are

sphere, **cylinder**, **cone**, **cuboid** and **cube**.

Put the correct name alongside each letter.

A _____   B _____   C _____

D _____   E _____

For solid A: How many edges has it? _____

How many faces has it? _____

How many corners has it? _____

What is the shape of each face? _____

For solid B: How many edges has it? _____

How many faces has it? _____

How many corners has it? _____

What is the shape of each face? _____

Use this rectangle and
the dots to help you
draw a cuboid.

Shopping

10p CHOCO

LOLLY 15p

CONE 20p

Oranges 5p each

What is the cost?

  Fill in the answers.

1 2 oranges

_____p

2 2 lollies

_____p

3 9 chocos

_____p

4 3 cones

_____p

5 3 lollies _____p
   2 chocos _____p
   Total _____p

6 3 cones _____p
   2 oranges _____p
   Total _____p

7 4 lollies _____p
   1 orange _____p
   Total _____p

8 2 cones _____p
   3 lollies _____p
   1 choco _____p
   Total _____p

9 2 oranges _____p
   1 choco _____p
   3 cones _____p
   Total _____p

10 3 oranges _____p
   1 cone _____p
   2 chocos _____p
   Total _____p

11 How many chocos can I buy for 50p? _____

12 How many cones can I buy for £1? _____

13 How many oranges can I buy with £1? _____

14 How many chocos can I buy with £1? _____

Fifty pence

This is a 50p coin.

Two of them are worth £1.

 Write in the missing numbers.

From 50p I spend	40p	30p	20p	10p
My change will be	10p	p	p	p

From 50p I spend	45p	35p	25p	15p	5p
My change will be	p	p	p	p	p

 Write the answers.

33p + 17p   23p + 27p   13p + 37p   3p + 47p
= ☐ p   = ☐ p   = ☐ p   = ☐ p

50p − 19p   50p − 29p   50p − 39p   50p − 49p
= ☐ p   = ☐ p   = ☐ p   = ☐ p

50p − 42p   50p − 32p   50p − 22p   50p − 12p
= ☐ p   = ☐ p   = ☐ p   = ☐ p

5p × 10   10p × 5   25p + 25p   ½ of £1
= ☐ p   = ☐ p   = ☐ p   = ☐ p

My change from 50p was 41p. How much did I pay? ☐ p

A pen cost 19p. How much change will I need from 50p? ☐ p

Litres

4 cups can be
filled from 1 litre.

Each cup holds ¼ litre.

 Write the number of cups.

1	2	3	4	5	6	7	8	litres
4								cups.

will fill

From 1½ litres I can fill ☐ cups.

From 2½ litres I can fill ☐ cups.

 Write the number of litres.

4	6	8	10	12	14	16	cups can be
	1½						litres.

filled from

What fraction of a litre is 2 cups? ☐

 Write the number of cups which can be filled from:

1	2	3	4	5	6	7	½-litre cartons.
	4					14	cups

 Write in the missing numbers.

1	2	3	4	2-litre cartons
8				cups.

will fill

Which is the larger, 5 cups or 2 litres? _____

Answers

To Parents:

We have not provided *all* the answers here. We suggest that items to be drawn should be checked by you. In the case of activities where calculations are performed by your child, it would be good practice to get him/her to use a calculator to check the answers.

Page 2

6	9 12 15 18	6	8 10	14 16 18
9 12	18 21	8 10 12	16 18 20
12 15 18 21 24	10 12 14	18 20 22
15 18 21 27	12 14 16	20 22 24

16 19 22	20 23 26	22 25 28
19 22 25	23 26 29	25 28 31
22 25 28	26 29 32	28 31 34

0 4 8 12 16	10 11 12 13 14 15
4 8 12 16 20	11 12 13 14 15 16
8 12 16 20 24	12 13 14 15 16 17
12 16 20 24 28	13 14 15 16 17 18

Page 3

20, 4, 60, 30, 70

4, 2

5, 15, 25, 3, 4, 2, 20

Page 4

32, 66, 13, 44
101, 99

forty-one	thirty-three
nineteen	forty-three
ninety-nine	seventy
twenty	three hundred
six	six hundred
one hundred	nine hundred
nine	eighty
seven hundred	eight hundred

Page 5

4 7 10
5 8 11
6 9 12
2 5 8
3 6 9
4 7 10
12 8 4 9 10 21
9 8 9 10 16 11

Page 6

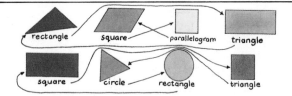

rectangle	square	parallelogram	triangle
square	circle	rectangle	triangle

3, 4, 5, 6   3, 4, 5, 6   triangle, rectangle, pentagon, hexagon

Page 7

1
```
 |11
 | 9
11 9|
```
2
```
 |18
 | 4
10 12|22
```
3
```
 |20
 | 7
13 14|27
```
4
```
 | 5
 | 9
 | 8
10 8 4|22
```
5
```
 |10
 |10
 | 7
8 11 8|27
```
6
```
 |12
 |12
 | 5
13 10 6|29
```
7
```
 |11
 |12
 |12
 |11
10 10 14 12|46
```
8
```
 |10
 |10
 |10
 |10
4 8 12 16|40
```
9
```
 |12
 |20
 |16
 | 8
14 14 14 14|56
```

Page 8

59, 70, 60, 406
40, 89, 91
50, 70, 120
50, 20, 10
50, 50, 20

Page 9

2 3
4 2
1 2
2 1
1 5
2, 1 5, 1
2, 5, 1

Page 10

11, 29, 17, 99
23, 21, 20
25, 8
19
23
42

Page 11

18, 18, 17
14, 0, 1
8, 8, 7
4, 4, 4
7, 18, 11
3, 5, 5
7, 1, 1, 2
9, 8, 7, 6
11 4

Page 12

6 8	21 24 27
6 9 12	28 32 36
8 12 16	35 40 45
10 15	42 48 54

0 0 0 0	1 3 5 7
0 4 8 12	3 9 15 21
0 8 16 24	5 15 25 35
0 12 24 36	7 21 35 49

6 8 10 12	5 7 9
12 16 20 24	10 14 18
18 24 30 36	15 21 27
24 32 40 48	20 28 36
30 40 50 60	25 35 45

5 10 15 20	9 6 18 15
9 18 27 36	15 10 30 25
6 12 18 24	21 14 42 35

6 8 10 12
12 16 20 24
18 24 30 36

Page 13

²⁄₅
³⁄₅
¼, ¾, ⅔, ⅓
½ past 3, ¼ to six

Page 14

6, 10, 4
0, 2, 12, 8
14   2 × 2 + 3 + 5 = 12
8 6 12
10 40 14 56

Page 15

2, 10, 2
10, 10, 4

Page 16

3, 3, 3   5, 5, 5
12   20
2, 2, 2, 2   6, 6
8   12
10, 10, 10   8, 8, 8
30   24
5, 5, 5, 5, 5, 5, 30
6, 6, 6, 6, 6, 30
4, 4, 4, 4, 4, 4, 4, 28
15, 15, 16
18, 18, 20
18, 24, 21

Page 17

10, 8, 9, 8
6, 3, 9, 4

Page 18

10, 15, 20   10 to 12
15, 15, 60   ¼ to 2

Page 19

is more than	is equal to
is more than	is less than
is equal to	is equal to

80, 84, 76
84, 76
12, 20, 20, 7

Page 20

40, 50, 60
70, 80, 90
5, 25, 1
3, 1, 1½
20, 2, 40, 4
30, 3, 80, 8

Page 21

31
Thurs
10th
Tues
8th
Satur
12th

Page 22

2, 4, 6, 2
5, 3, 8, 4
7, 2, 2, 9
7, 7, 7, 4
9
9
4, 2

Page 23

	35	120
	40	65
100	75	185
120	120	65
40	35	40
160	155	105
65	40	120
35	35	65
30	5	55

Page 13 (continued)

65	120	120
40	40	35
25	80	85
260		

Page 24

2, 10
4, 1
2, 10
12, 14
16, 18
5, 5
2, 1

Page 25

6, 8, 8

Page 27

10, 6
3, 2
2, 1
16
4

Page 26

5, 2
5, 2
10, 10
2, 2
5, 2
30, 27, 26
A
C
1, 4

Page 28

A Cube, B Cuboid, C Sphere
D Cylinder, E Cone
12
6
8
Square
12
6
8
Rectangle

Page 29

10, 30, 90, 60		
45	60	60
20	10	5
65	70	65
40	10	15
45	10	20
10	60	20
95	80	55
5		
5		
20		
10		

Page 30

20, 30, 40
5, 15, 25, 35, 45
50, 50, 50, 50
31, 21, 11, 1
8, 18, 28, 38
50, 50, 50, 50
9
31

Page 31

8, 12, 16, 20, 24, 28, 32
6
10
1, 2, 2½, 3, 3½, 4
½
2, 6, 8, 10, 12
16, 24, 32
2 litres